THE
COLORS
OF NATURE

A COLOR, DRAW, & SKETCH BOOK
FOR ALL THINGS WILD & FREE

LEISURE ARTS, INC. • Maumelle, Arkansas

Published by Leisure Arts, Inc.
Produced by Better Day Books.
Illustrations copyright © 2019 Lindsay Hopkins.

We have made every effort to ensure that these instructions are accurate and complete. We cannot, however, be responsible for human error, typographical mistakes, or variations in individual work.

Acquisition and Content Development—Peg Couch, Better Day Books;
Instructional Text—Lindsay Hopkins; Editorial Text—Peg Couch and
Katie Weeber; Graphic Design—Michael Douglas.

Made in USA.

It's a Good Day to Have a Better Day

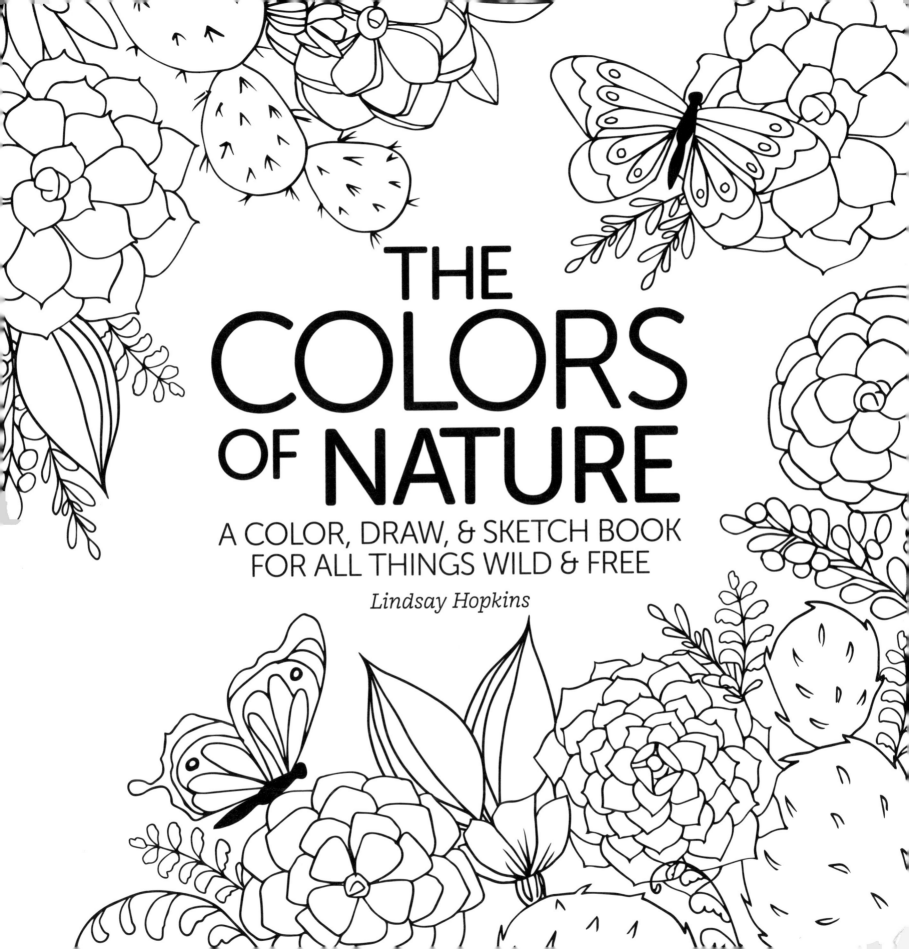

THE COLORS OF NATURE

A COLOR, DRAW, & SKETCH BOOK FOR ALL THINGS WILD & FREE

Lindsay Hopkins

CONTENTS

COLOR, DRAW, & JOURNAL!

HELLO,

If you have found this book, then you must love plants and flowers as much as I do.

From wild daisies growing on grassy roadsides to tiny succulents planted in pretty, little pots—I am always inspired by the colors, textures, and varieties that nature has to offer. That's why I am so happy to provide my interpretation of some beautiful plants to inspire *your own* creativity.

Inside you will find 15 popular plants and flowers to color along with an overview that provides coloring tips and interesting traits and symbolism of each (did you know that dahlias represent elegance and dignity?). Also included are drawing lessons. As adult coloring has become so popular, I've noticed that more and more people are interested in taking their creativity to the next level. So, I have broken each plant or flower down into 4 easy drawing steps and provided space for you to practice. Be brave and try it! Most people are way more creative than they give themselves credit for! Finally, each section concludes with a journal page that has more sketches to color and an area where you can record field notes—when and where you saw the flower in nature.

So, whether you are relaxed in a comfy chair coloring with a cup of tea... or out-and-about coloring in nature... I hope this book will inspire you to take a moment to smell the roses, and the sunflowers, and peonies....

Join me on social media to share your coloring.
You can find me @pen_and_paint!

Live a colorful life,

Lindsay

7

Bluebell

Legend holds that bluebells are used by fairies to call one another to their gatherings. These whimsical flowers certainly bring to mind an enchanting woodland clearing after the chill of winter has passed.

Bluebells come in every shade of blue imaginable, as well as purple, pink, and white. To add depth and realism to your art, experiment with shading and layering colors to capture all the hues represented in these flowers.

Bluebells are lovely displayed on their own, but their gentle curved shape also makes them a lovely addition to other arrangements, spilling over the edges of a vase. Try pairing them with other flowers in shades of pink, blue, and purple for a simple springtime arrangement.

Bluebells are a beautiful expression of love, representing ongoing faithfulness and steadfastness. They are perfect for Mother's Day and other springtime events.

the earth laughs in flowers.

—R.W. EMERSON

STEP 1: Draw a horizontal curved line with small curved lines branching out from the bottom to form a stem for the bluebells.

STEP 2: On the top side draw two accent leaves.

STEP 3: Draw small bell shaped flowers at the end of each curved line to form a row of bluebells.

STEP 4: Finish by drawing accent buds and lines for the bluebells.

Step 1

Step 2

Step 3

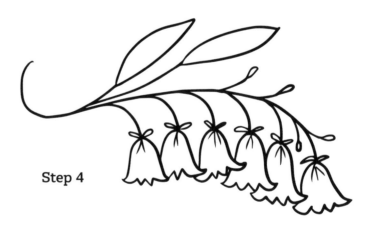

Step 4

Practice

START HERE: Try your first drawing by using this pattern at left to trace. Then in the available space below, draw a few more Bluebells freehand.

Observe

DATE: _____

PLACE: _____

NOTES: _____

_____

_____

_____

Sketch what you've
observed in nature here!

Buttercup

No flower could be more perfectly suited to its name than the buttercup. The bright cheerful color reminds us of the sunniest days of summer, and it's a pleasure to come across clusters of these cute blooms growing in the wild.

The buttercup's natural colors are yellow and green, although there are varieties available in pink, red, and orange. When coloring buttercups, take the opportunity to experiment with all the shades of yellow available to you, from light cream to rich gold.

Buttercups were made for mason jars and similar containers. If you'd like to include other flowers or accents, deep shades of blue and purple will help set off the buttercups' vibrant yellow.

Buttercups are all about happiness and positivity. They also remind us of childhood innocence. Pair these flowers with joyful occasions like a housewarming, homecoming, or birth of a child. Buttercups also make lovely decorations for a springtime garden party.

Life is the flower for which love is the honey.

—VICTOR HUGO

STEP 1: Begin with a small round shape with curved edges to form the center of the buttercup.

STEP 2: Draw separate curved edges all around the center of the buttercup.

STEP 3: Draw buttercup petals all around the center, layering them as you go; add in accent lines from the center of the flower.

STEP 4: On the side of the buttercup draw an adjoining leaf.

Step 1

Step 2

Step 3

Step 4

Practice

START HERE: Try your first drawing by using this pattern at left to trace. Then in the available space below, draw a few more Buttercups freehand.

DATE: _____

PLACE: _____

NOTES: _____

_____

_____

_____

_____

Sketch what you've observed in nature here!

Cactus

Cacti are some of nature's most beautiful and surprising plants. From the mighty saguaro standing tall in the desert to tiny houseplants sitting on sunny kitchen windowsills, they never fail to impress (spines and all!).

Cacti come in a vast array of hues from light and dark green to shades of gray and even blue, while their dramatic flowers bloom in gorgeous pinks, oranges, yellows, and reds. When coloring, try using a monochromatic color scheme for the cactus body and bright, bold colors for the flowers.

Cacti are perfect houseplants for those without a green thumb as they require only simple care. Collect several varieties and plant them in small textured containers to add a relaxed Bohemian vibe to your space.

Cacti represent longevity and endurance. They live for a long time and will therefore remind the receiver of your unconditional love and commitment. Be brave and give one to someone today.

All good things are wild & free.

—HENRY DAVID THOREAU

STEP 1: Begin by drawing a large balloon shape with a flat bottom to form the cactus.

STEP 2: From the top center draw curved lines connecting to the bottom of the cactus.

STEP 3: At the top of the cactus draw in petals to form a bloom.

STEP 4: Finish by drawing random spines on the edges and lines of the cactus.

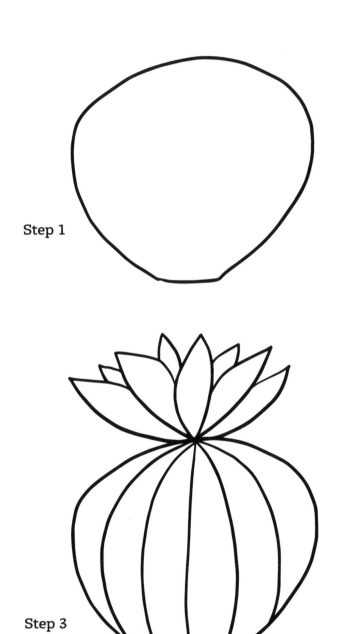

Step 1

Step 2

Step 3

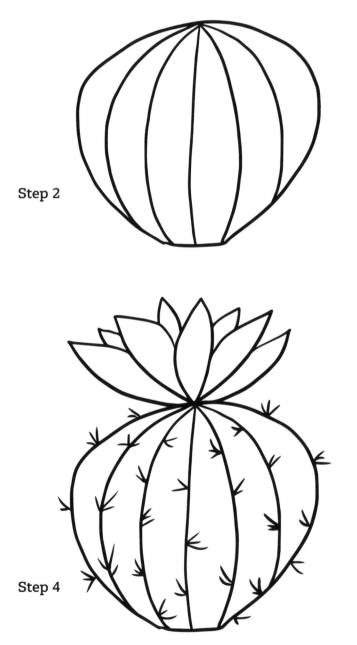

Step 4

Practice

START HERE: Try your first drawing by using this pattern at left to trace. Then in the available space below, draw a few more Cacti freehand.

DATE: _____

PLACE: _____

NOTES: _____

_____

_____

_____

*Sketch what you've
observed in nature here!*

Dahlia

Just when our favorite springtime flowers begin to fade, dahlias burst into bloom with a flourish of color. These fascinating flowers capture the imagination, with shapes like round, fluffy pompoms and immense dinnerplates.

Many dahlias have multicolored petals, with bright highlights at the edges transitioning to rich hues at the flower's center. This provides the perfect opportunity to experiment with blending to recreate this natural beauty.

A single dahlia can be quite impressive all on its own. Try displaying large blooms in individual vases or glasses. You can also trim the stems of several dahlias to about an inch long and float the blooms in a bowl of water.

With their rows and rows of perfectly arranged petals, dahlias remind us of elegance and dignity. Their large blooms and vibrant colors stand out from the crowd, encouraging us to stay true to ourselves and embrace what makes us unique.

Adopt the pace of nature; her secret is patience.

—R.W. EMERSON

STEP 1: Begin by drawing a row of thin vertical ovals to create the center of the dahlia.

STEP 2: Draw three curved lines behind the ovals and begin with the first layer of petals for the dahlia.

STEP 3: Draw in only one row of petals for the back of the dahlia, and draw two rows of petals for the front portion.

STEP 4: Draw in two more rows of petals in the front, layering each. Finish the dahlia with a stem and leaf.

Step 1

Step 2

Step 3

Step 4

Practice

START HERE: Try your first drawing by using this pattern at left to trace. Then in the available space below, draw a few more Dahlias freehand.

DATE: _____

PLACE: _____

NOTES: _____

_____

_____

_____

Sketch what you've observed in nature here!

Daisy

Whether it's the pure white petals, the bright yellow centers, or the way they grow in happy bunches along the roadside— we just can't resist daisies!

When coloring daisies, it's fun to explore all varieties and color options. The gerbera is one of the most popular types of daisy, with bright, beautiful hues like red, orange, coral, pink, and yellow. Use your creativity to come up with a palette that pleases you and your imagination.

Daisies add a touch whimsy and unassuming beauty wherever we use them. They're fun to arrange and pair well with so many other flowers. For a laidback country look, place a few daisies in a small white pitcher and finish it off with a blue gingham ribbon.

Daisies are associated with innocence and purity. They remind us of carefree summer days spent weaving flower crowns or gently removing each petal while playing "loves me, loves me not." They make perfect gifts for a Sweet 16 birthday or an expectant mom.

Just living is not enough... one must have sunshine, freedom, and a little flower.

—HANS CHRISTIAN ANDERSON

STEP 1: Begin by drawing lots of tiny circles to create the center of the daisy.

STEP 2: Draw a single row of daisy petals around the center.

STEP 3: Draw accent lines on petals starting at the base of the center.

STEP 4: On the side of the daisy draw adjoining leaves.

Step 1

Step 2

Step 3

Step 4

Practice

START HERE: Try your first drawing by using this pattern at left to trace. Then in the available space below, draw a few more Daisies freehand.

DATE: _____

PLACE: _____

NOTES: _____

_____

_____

_____

Sketch what you've observed in nature here!

Fern

All the shady, quiet areas in nature are blanketed with ferns, from forest clearings to riverbanks to rocky hillsides. Their soft, feathery leaves are mesmerizing rustling in the wind, helping us appreciate the beauty of the moment.

Most ferns are green, although there are several varieties that initially produce fronds in pink, yellow, orange, or red before the plant matures. Even if you'd prefer to use green for your coloring, you can experiment with all the different shades available, from teal to evergreen and everything in between.

Potted ferns are a common choice for houseplants as they are very easy to care for. Use ferns in arrangements to create a full, but subtle backdrop for more vibrant flowers.

Ferns remind us of sincerity and steadfastness. They're always right where we expect them to be and make us feel sure of ourselves. Give a fern to a friend or partner to remind them that you will always be there for them.

If you look the right way, you can see the whole world is a garden.

—FRANCES HODGSON BURNETT

STEP 1: Draw three curved lines to form the fern frond.

STEP 2: On two of the fern fronds add leaves with curvy edges.

STEP 3: On the third frond draw thin leaves on each side to create an open frond.

STEP 4: Finish by adding a very curved line from the base of the fern to create a fiddlehead.

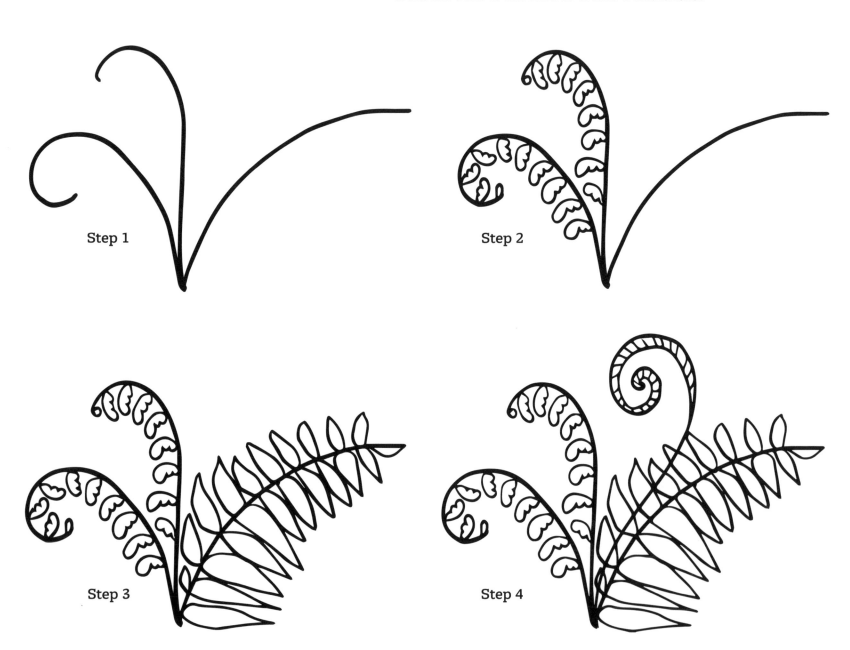

Step 1

Step 2

Step 3

Step 4

Practice

START HERE: Try your first drawing by using this pattern at left to trace. Then in the available space below, draw a few more Ferns freehand.

Observe

DATE: _____

PLACE: _____

NOTES: _____

_____

_____

_____

Sketch what you've observed in nature here!

Monstera

From its large waxy leaves to its hooded flowers and distinctive fruit, the monstera plant is completely unique. Images of this tropical beauty bring to mind lush rainforests and exotic beaches.

If you're up for a challenge, try to capture the shiny appearance of the monstera's leaves. Use your lightest colors to create highlights and your darkest colors to create shadow. Although the monstera's flowers are naturally white, its leaves are often pictured with flowers in bright tropical colors like yellow, pink, and orange.

Monstera leaf arrangements will give your space a beachy, tropical vibe. Try placing a single, oversized leaf in a tall, thin decorative vase. Something with a mosaic or bold geometric print can enhance the captivating look of this plant.

This hearty plant does everything in a big way. In its natural habitat, it will rapidly climb up trees that are 60 feet tall. Monstera reminds us to reach for our dreams and never stop growing. While monstera is a popular houseplant, make sure your recipient has room for this exuberant plant before giving it as a gift.

Nature does not hurry, yet everything is accomplished.

—LAO TZU

STEP 1: Begin by drawing a vertical curved line to form the stem of the monstera.

STEP 2: Draw large leaf around the stem with various opening splits.

STEP 3: Draw a variety of small holes in the monstera leaf.

STEP 4: Finish by drawing accent lines from stem outward.

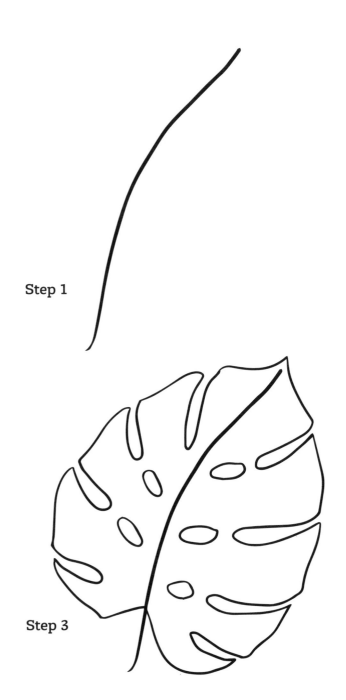

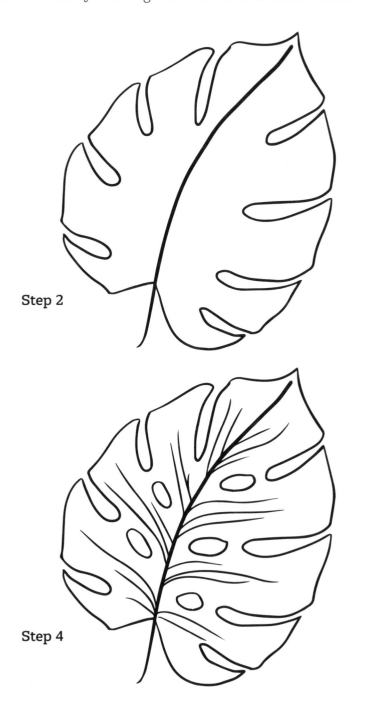

Step 1

Step 2

Step 3

Step 4

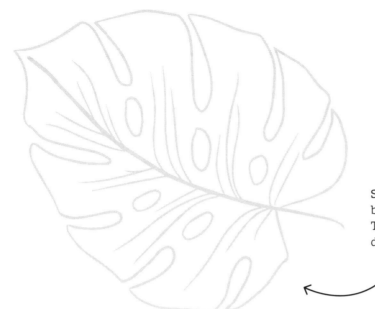

Practice

START HERE: Try your first drawing by using this pattern at left to trace. Then in the available space below, draw a few more Monsteras freehand.

DATE: _____

PLACE: _____

NOTES: _____

_____

_____

_____

_____

*Sketch what you've
observed in nature here!*

Mum

When mums start appearing on your neighbors' doorsteps, you know fall is just around the corner. These lush plants look right at home with haybales and pumpkins in beautiful colors that match the changing leaves.

You will often see mums in rusty orange and rich burgundy, but they also bloom in white, cream, yellow, pink, and lavender. Sometimes, garden centers will plant two or three varieties in the same pot, producing an eclectic mix of color.

Mums are as lovely indoors as they are outdoors. They're a quick and easy way to brighten up an entryway or dress up a Thanksgiving table. Just grab a handful of button mums in any color and pop them in a vase. A galvanized metal container will add to the rustic fall look.

Mums represent hope and joy, making them a wonderful gift for anyone entering a new stage in life, like a graduate, newlywed, or new parent. Mums help express your wishes for good things to come in the future.

We can never have enough of Nature.

—HENRY DAVID THOREAU

STEP 1: Begin by drawing small tear drop shapes connecting to form the center of the mum, adding several rows of curved lines around the center.

STEP 2: Draw two rows of longer petals from the center of the mum.

STEP 3: Draw another two rows of longer petals, layering behind the first two rows to complete the mum.

STEP 4: Finish by draw adjoining leaves on the side of the mum.

Step 1

Step 2

Step 3

Step 4

Practice

START HERE: Try your first drawing by using this pattern at left to trace. Then in the available space below, draw a few more mums freehand.

Observe

DATE: _____

PLACE: _____

NOTES: _____

_____

_____

_____

*Sketch what you've
observed in nature here!*

Peony

Ah, the beautiful peony! From gardeners to interior designers to wedding planners, everyone loves this flower. Although they come in many colors such as white, coral, red, and even yellow, peonies are most commonly remembered for their romantic pink hues.

Because they're packed with petals, peonies provide lots of opportunities for you to explore creative coloring. Experiment with various layers of color and shading to add interest and depth to your art.

Peonies are the perfect centerpiece for a romantic dinner alfresco. When arranging them, less is more. Try a simple vase with a fresh sprig of eucalyptus to enhance their beauty. Add a special someone, a starry night, and a glass of chilled rosé to complete the scene!

Peonies symbolize romance and prosperity. They are a timeless and traditional favorite for weddings and anniversaries. Give peonies in shades of pink to symbolize love and deep hues of red to wish someone good fortune.

I must have flowers always & always.

—CLAUDE MONET

STEP 1: Draw a small circle to form the center of the peony.

STEP 2: Add an 'X' shape in the circle.

STEP 3: Draw one larger loose petal curved one at the bottom and two additional petals layered on the sides.

STEP 4: Continue by adding loose petals around the center, with some curving up and out.

Step 1

Step 2

Step 3

Step 4

Practice

START HERE: Try your first drawing by using this pattern at left to trace. Then in the available space below, draw a few more Peonies freehand.

Observe

DATE: _____

PLACE: _____

NOTES: _____

_____

_____

_____

Sketch what you've observed in nature here!

Poppy

Poppies are often found growing wild, and fields of red poppies are an iconic and powerful image. Poppies are especially precious because of their short blooming season. Some varieties bloom only for about four weeks.

While red poppies are probably the most well-known, you have loads of options for coloring these flowers. Poppies can be found in white and cream, yellow, orange, pink, and even some shades of blue and purple. Many of them have bright yellow centers.

Like many wildflowers, poppies are a natural fit for rustic décor. Choose poppies in complimentary colors and arrange them in milk jugs of several different sizes to create a simple but elegant display.

Especially in Europe, red poppies are used for Remembrance or Armistice Day, which recognizes the end of World War I. Poppies can be used to honor a loved one who has passed away or to acknowledge someone going through a difficult time.

a flower blossoms for its own joy.

—OSCAR WILDE

STEP 1: Draw a medium sized circle to create the center of the poppy and add tear drops to form a star shape in the center of the circle.

STEP 2: Draw small scalloped lines around the edge of the circle.

STEP 3: Draw five petals of the poppy overlapping them as you go around the center.

STEP 4: Finish by drawing multiple lines on each petal from the center of the poppy outwards, and add leaves on the side of the flower.

Step 1

Step 2

Step 3

Step 4

Practice

START HERE: Try your first drawing by using this pattern at left to trace. Then in the available space below, draw a few more Poppies freehand.

DATE: _____

PLACE: _____

NOTES: _____

_____

_____

_____

*Sketch what you've
observed in nature here!*

Rose

The rose is without doubt the most beloved flower and unmatched in popularity. It's soft velvety petals, heavenly scent, and delicate blooms have attracted avid gardeners and romantics to them for centuries—regardless of the thorns and sharp toothed leaves!

There are more than 100 varieties of roses. In addition to red and white, they bloom in endless shades of pink, yellow, orange, and lavender, providing a wide spectrum of coloring opportunities!

With all the varieties and colors, there are endless ways to present roses. Try cutting the stems to different lengths, starting with short stems and adding longer ones for a tiered arrangement. Use simple greenery as an accent, or let the flowers stand on their own.

The red rose is synonymous with love and glamour, but other colors hold different associations—white for honor and innocence, yellow for friendship and joy, pink for gratitude and admiration. No matter what you're trying to express, there's a rose to match your message!

Love blooms where hope grows

—AUTHOR UNKNOWN

STEP 1: Begin with a small circle for the center of the rose. Add three small lines joining in the center.

STEP 2: Starting from the center draw three rows of petals layering each row behind the other.

STEP 3: At the tip of each rose petal add in a curved accent line.

STEP 4: On the side of the rose draw adjoining leaves.

Step 1

Step 2

Step 3

Step 4

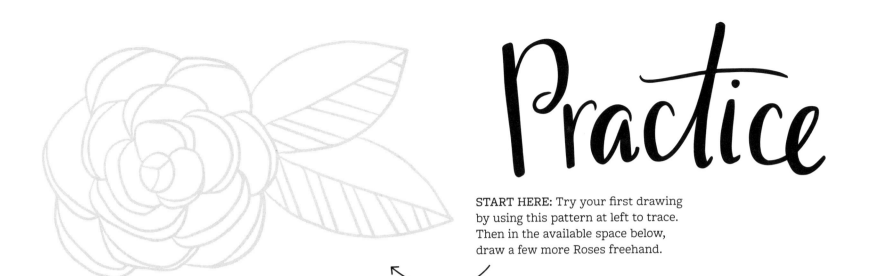

Practice

START HERE: Try your first drawing by using this pattern at left to trace. Then in the available space below, draw a few more Roses freehand.

DATE: _____

PLACE: _____

NOTES: _____

_____

_____

_____

*Sketch what you've
observed in nature here!*

Succulents

These trendy little plants are as unique as they are adorable with their quirky shapes, interesting textures, and range of colors. It's impossible to pick just one!

A cool color palette is perfect for succulents, which are commonly found in shades of green, blue, and purple. Several varieties come in bold red or have accents in yellow and orange at the tips of their petals. The layered leaves provide a perfect opportunity to experiment with different shading techniques.

Succulents look wonderful planted together. Gather a collection with different shapes, textures, and colors, and display them together in a square or rectangular planter box.

With their ability to thrive in harsh climates, succulents are a perfect representation of endless love and can remind us of our inner strength. Succulents are inexpensive and low-maintenance, making these charming plants perfect party favors.

To plant a garden is to believe in tomorrow

—AUDREY HEPBURN

STEP 1: Begin by drawing a small sideways 'e' shape for the center of the succulent.

STEP 2: From the center draw curved lines that create a tip to form four succulent leaves.

STEP 3: Continue adding leaves in rows until you have formed four layers of the succulent.

STEP 4: Finish the succulent by added random curved lines on various leaves to add depth.

Step 1

Step 2

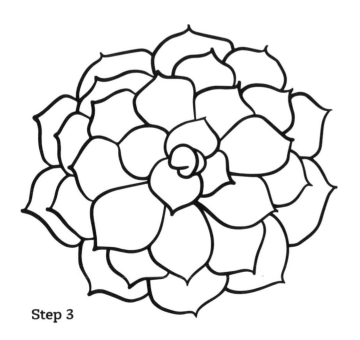

Step 3

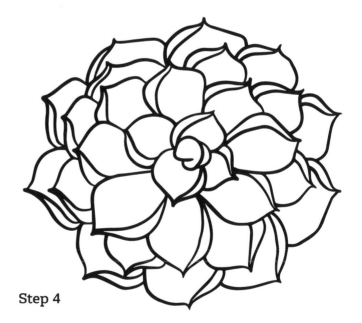

Step 4

Practice

START HERE: Try your first drawing by using this pattern at left to trace. Then in the available space below, draw a few more Succulents freehand.

DATE: _____

PLACE: _____

NOTES: _____

_____

_____

_____

*Sketch what you've
observed in nature here!*

Sunflower

The last days of summer are perfect for lazy creek-side picnics, sipping lemonade on the front porch, and gazing at endless fields of sunflowers.

With their big, bold flower heads, irrepressible sunflowers remind us to stand tall and face the sun. Sunflowers are most commonly associated with bright yellow petals, but they also come in gorgeous shades of red, brown, and orange. So be creative with your coloring and explore lots of options!

Sunflowers can be easily found at farmer's markets, grocery stores, and—if you're lucky—a roadside stand. Simply cut a few stems and pop them into a mason jar. Add some wildflowers in a complementary shade and finish your arrangement with a natural jute cord.

Sunflowers symbolize positivity and optimism. They're the perfect flower to send to someone in need of a pick-me-up. They're also great for decorating carefree summer brunches, casual backyard parties, and even late summer outdoor weddings.

Keep your face to the sunshine & you cannot see the shadows. It's what the sunflowers do.

—HELEN KELLER

STEP 1: Draw a medium sized circle for the center of the sunflower.

STEP 2: Within the circle repeat drawing small circles to create the seeds of the sunflower.

STEP 3: Draw a layer of petals around the center of the sunflower.

STEP 4: Complete the sunflower with a second layer of petals. Finish with accent lines on petals starting at the base of the center.

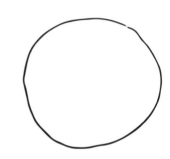

Step 1

Step 2

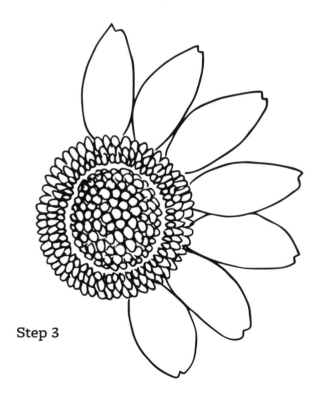

Step 3

Step 4

Practice

START HERE: Try your first drawing by using this pattern at left to trace. Then in the available space below, draw a few more Sunflowers freehand.

DATE: _____

PLACE: _____

NOTES: _____

_____

_____

_____

*Sketch what you've
observed in nature here!*

Tulip

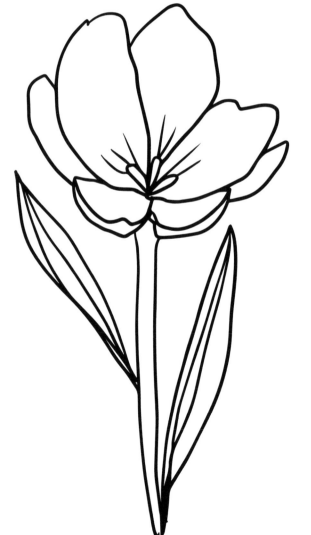

Tulips are the ambassadors of spring, blooming in our gardens to welcome the change of season. With their sturdy stature, unique shape, and array of colors, tulips are one of the most iconic flowers.

When it comes to coloring tulips, you have endless options. Tulips bloom in deep shades of purple and violet, vibrant pinks and reds, bright oranges and yellows, and soft creams and white. There are even varieties with multicolored petals.

To create a simple, classic arrangement, use tulips of the same color or a range of similar colors like yellows, oranges, and reds. Or, combine all the colors you can find for an exuberant springtime bouquet. Tulips pair beautifully with field greens and eucalyptus.

Tulips are most commonly associated with love, although different colors can represent different things, like yellow for happiness. Because of their arrival in spring, they are also associated with rebirth. Potted tulips are a wonderful way to express your love or brighten someone's day.

there are always flowers for those who want to see them.

—HENRI MATISSE

STEP 1: Begin with a tilted oval to form a petal of the tulip.

STEP 2: Draw two petals layered on either side of the first tulip petal.

STEP 3: Draw two back petals layered behind your first three petals, and add accent lines at the base of the front petals.

STEP 4: From the base of the tulip add a stem and leaf.

Step 1

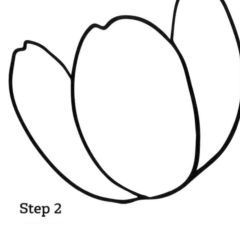

Step 2

Step 3

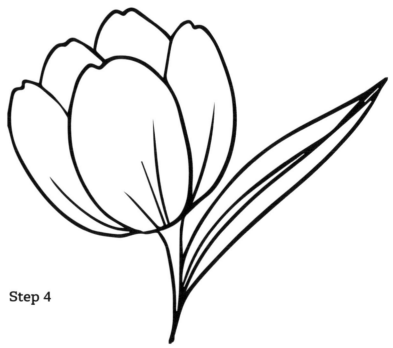

Step 4

Practice

START HERE: Try your first drawing by using this pattern at left to trace. Then in the available space below, draw a few more Tulips freehand.

Observe

DATE: _____

PLACE: _____

NOTES: _____

_____

_____

_____

*Sketch what you've
observed in nature here!*

Zinnia

Zinnias are a staple for gardeners, producing an abundance of color and attracting other visitors like bees, butterflies, and even hummingbirds. These cheerful blooms brighten our days from the end of summer through fall until the first frost arrives.

Zinnias come in an endless array of colors, with shades of yellow, orange, red, pink, purple, and even multi-colored blooms. Many varieties have rich deep colors at their centers surrounded by bright petals. Have fun playing with a variety of combinations in your coloring.

In the same family as daisies, zinnias are a fixture of rustic chic décor. Try grouping several bunches together by color and arranging them in a variety of white ceramic containers.

Zinnias have several different meanings, but almost all are associated with friendship and endurance. They make a wonderful thank-you gift and are the perfect way to let someone know you're thinking of them.

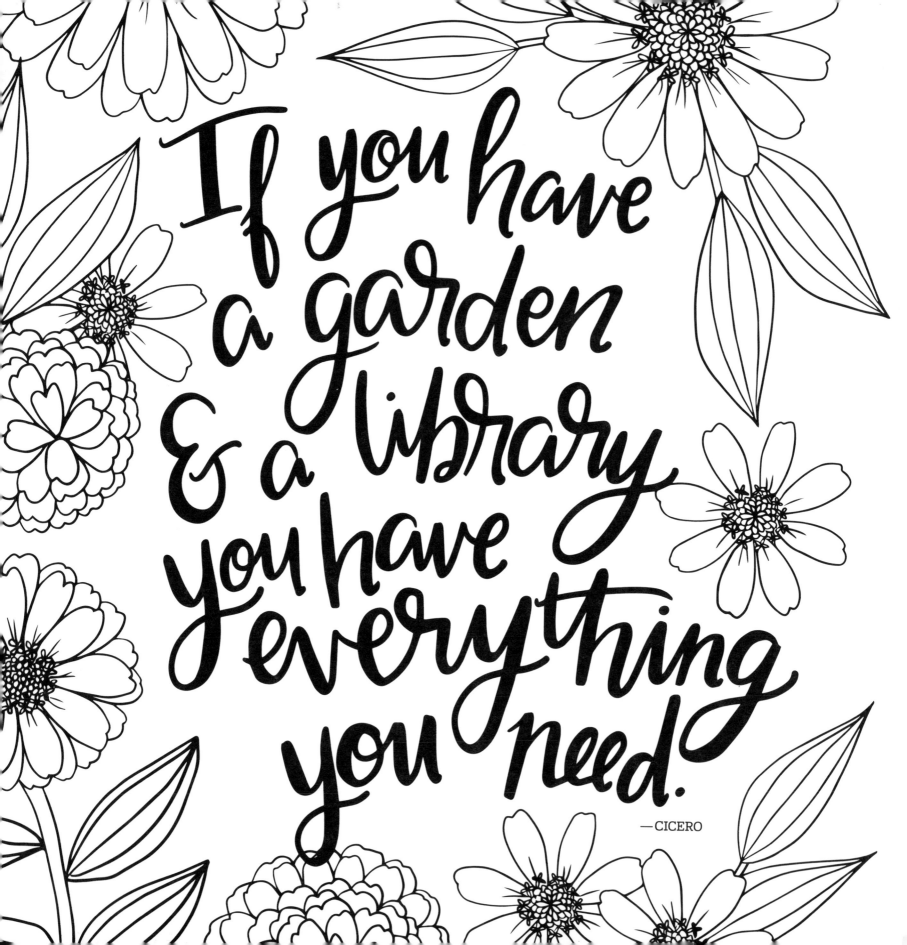

STEP 1: Begin by drawing small tear drop shapes connecting to form the center of the zinnia, adding several rows of curved lines around the center.

STEP 2: Add small 'X' shaped designs all the way around the center of the flower to create the pollen florets.

STEP 3: Add a single row of petals around the center of the zinnia.

STEP 4: Add a second row of petals behind the first, and add in accent lines on the first row of petals beginning at the base of the center.

Step 1

Step 2

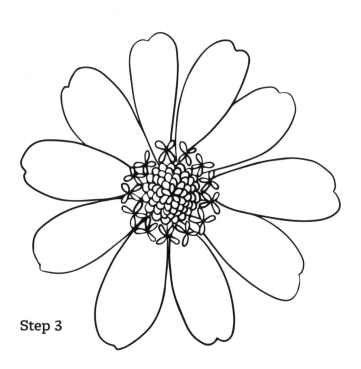

Step 3

Step 4

Practice

START HERE: Try your first drawing by using this pattern at left to trace. Then in the available space below, draw a few more Zinnias freehand.